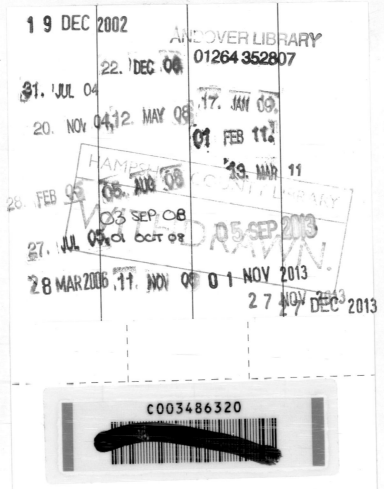

# EASIEST
# KEYBOARD
# COLLECTION

# Showstoppers

**WISE PUBLICATIONS**
London/New York/Paris/Sydney/Copenhagen/Madrid

Exclusive Distributors:

**Music Sales Limited**
8/9 Frith Street,
London W1V 5TZ, England.

**Music Sales Pty Limited**
120 Rothschild Avenue,
Rosebery, NSW 2018,
Australia..

Order No. AM944218
ISBN 0-7119-6603-6
This book © Copyright 1997 by Wise Publications

Cover design by Chloë Alexander
Compiled by Peter Evans
Music arranged by Derek Jones
Music processed by Paul Ewers Music Design

Printed in the United Kingdom by
Caligraving Limited, Thetford, Norfolk.

Cover photograph courtesy of:
Image Bank

Your Guarantee of Quality
As publishers, we strive to produce every book to the highest commercial
standards.
The music has been freshly engraved and the book has been carefully
designed to minimise awkward page turns and to make playing from it a
real pleasure.
Particular care has been given to specifying acid-free, neutral-sized paper
made from pulps which have not been elemental chlorine bleached. This
pulp is from farmed sustainable forests and was produced with special
regard for the environment.
Throughout, the printing and binding have been planned to ensure a
sturdy, attractive publication which should give years of enjoyment.
If your copy fails to meet our high standards, please inform us and we will
gladly replace it.

Music Sales' complete catalogue describes thousands of titles and is
available in full colour sections by subject, direct from Music Sales
Limited. Please state your areas of interest and send a cheque/postal
order for £1.50 for postage to: Music Sales Limited, Newmarket Road,
Bury St. Edmunds, Suffolk IP33 3YB.

# Contents

# AS LONG AS HE NEEDS ME

*Words & Music by Lionel Bart*

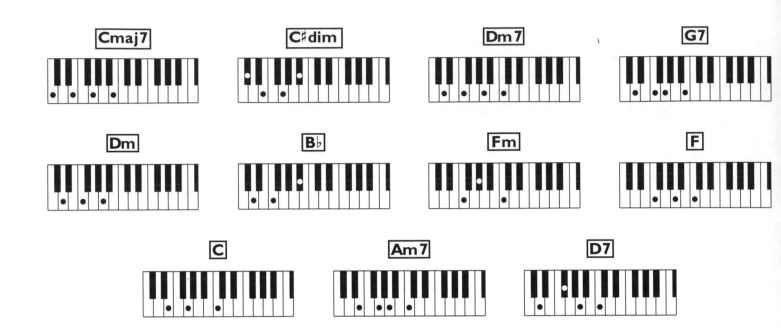

Voice: **Strings**

Rhythm: **Ballad**

Tempo: ♩ = 80

As long as he needs me I know where

I must be. I'll cling on stead - fast -

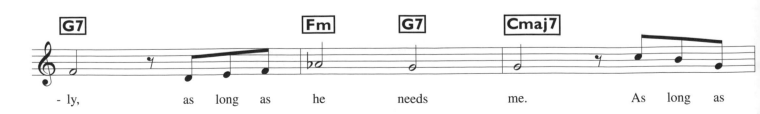

- ly, as long as he needs me. As long as

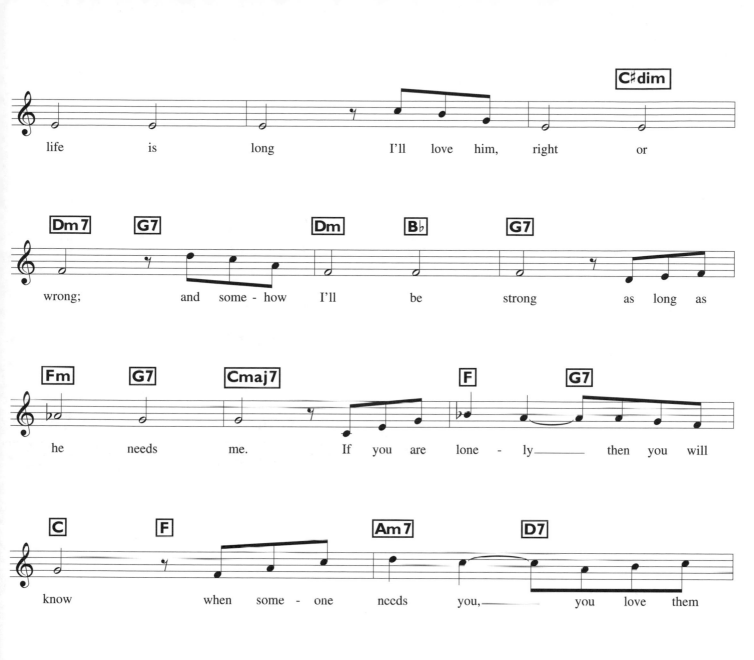

life is long I'll love him, right or

wrong; and some-how I'll be strong as long as

he needs me. If you are lone - ly————— then you will

know when some - one needs you,————— you love them

so. I won't be-tray this trust, though peo-ple

say I must. I've got to stay true

just as long as he needs me.

# A WONDERFUL DAY LIKE TODAY

*Words & Music by Leslie Bricusse & Anthony Newley*

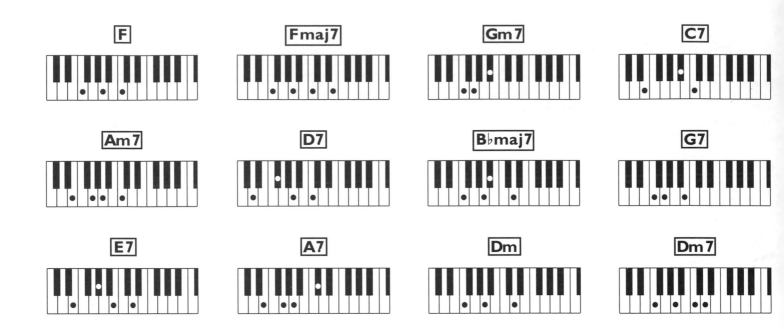

Voice: **Clarinet**

Rhythm: **March**

Tempo: ♩ = 84

On a won - der - ful day_____ like to -

- day,_____ I de - fy a - ny cloud_____ to ap -

- pear in the sky._____ Dare a - ny rain - drop to

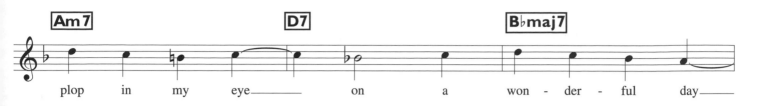

plop in my eye ___ on a won - der - ful day ___

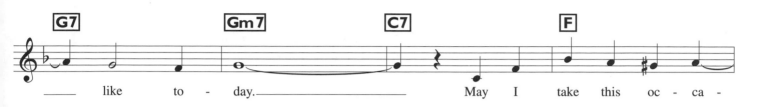

___ like to - day. ___ May I take this oc - ca -

- sion to say ___ that the whole hu - man race ___

___ should go down on it's knees, ___

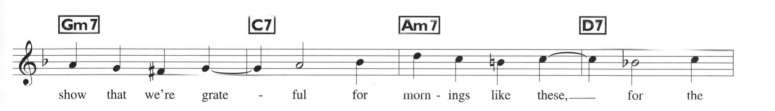

show that we're grate - ful for morn - ings like these, ___ for the

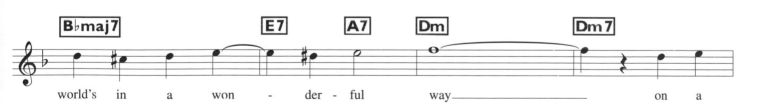

world's in a won - der - ful way ___ on a

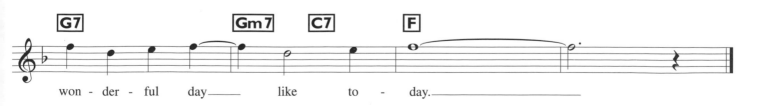

won - der - ful day ___ like to - day. ___

# CONSIDER YOURSELF

**Words & Music by Lionel Bart**

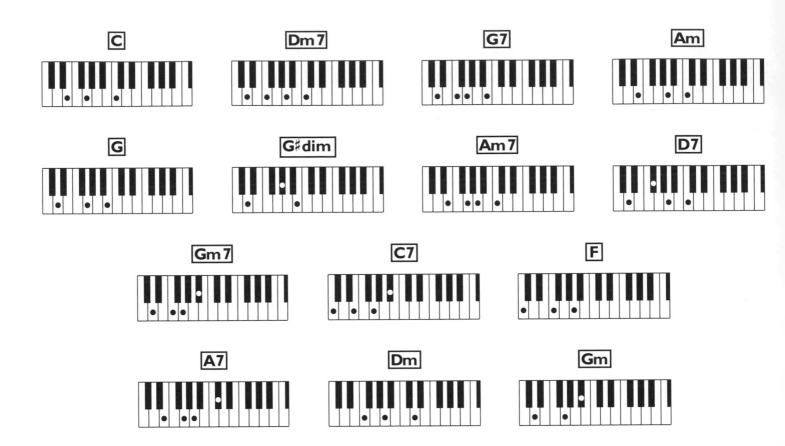

Voice: **Clarinet**

Rhythm: **2 Beat**

Tempo: ♩. = 104

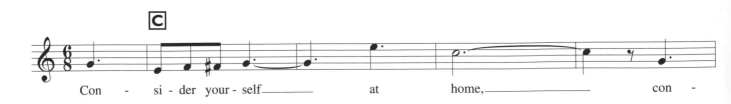

Con - si - der your - self_____ at home,_____ con -

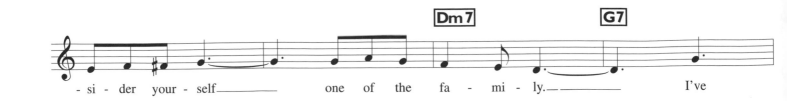

- si - der your - self_____ one of the fa - mi - ly._____ I've

ta - ken to you____ so strong,____ it's clear we're go-ing to get a -

long. If it should chance to be we should see some hard - er days,____ emp - ty

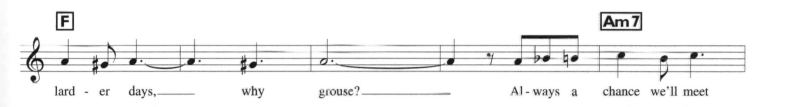

lard - er days,____ why grouse?_____ Al - ways a chance we'll meet

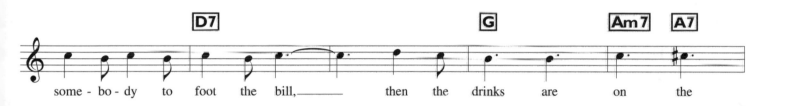

some - bo - dy to foot the bill,____ then the drinks are on the

house!_____ Con - si - der your - self____ our mate._____ We

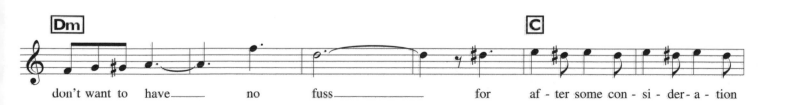

don't want to have____ no fuss_____ for af - ter some con - si - der - a - tion

we can state: Con - si - der your-self____ one of us.

# DIAMONDS ARE A GIRL'S BEST FRIEND

*Words by Leo Robin*
*Music by Jule Styne*

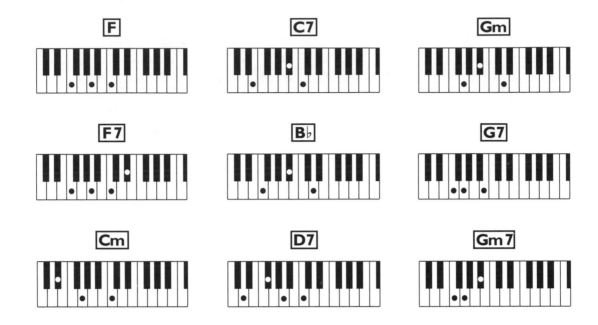

Voice:  **Trumpet**

Rhythm:  **March**

Tempo:  ♩ = 92

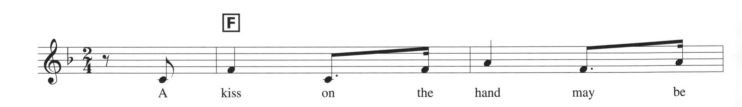

A kiss on the hand may be

quite con - ti - nen - tal, but dia - monds are a

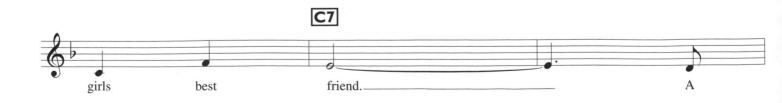

girls best friend._____ A

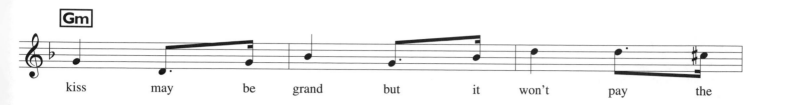

kiss may be grand but it won't pay the

rent - al on your hum - ble flat_____ or

help you at the au - to - mat. Men grow

cold as girls grow old and we all lose our

charms in the end._____ But square cut or

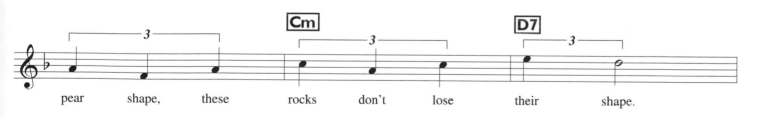

pear shape, these rocks don't lose their shape.

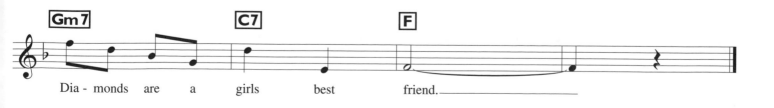

Dia - monds are a girls best friend._____

# DO YOU HEAR THE PEOPLE SING?

*Music by Claude-Michel Schönberg. Lyric by Herbert Kretzmer.*
*Original Text by Alain Boublil & Jean-Marc Natel*
© Copyright (Music & Lyrics) 1980 Editions Musicales Alain Boublil
English lyrics © Copyright 1985 Alain Boublil Music Limited.
This arrangement © Copyright 1997 Alain Boublil Music Limited.
All Rights Reserved. International Copyright Secured.

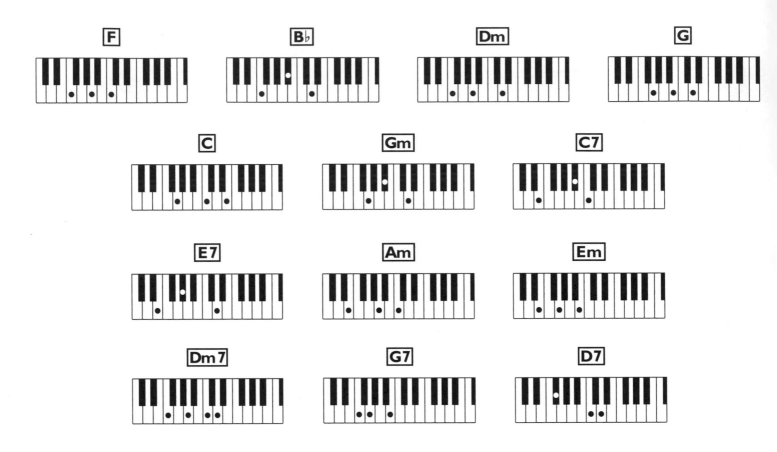

Voice: **Trumpet**

Rhythm: **March**

Tempo: ♩ = 76

Do you hear the peo - ple sing? Sing-ing the song of an - gry men. It is the

mu - sic of a peo - ple who will not be slaves a - gain! When the beat-ing of your heart ech-oes the

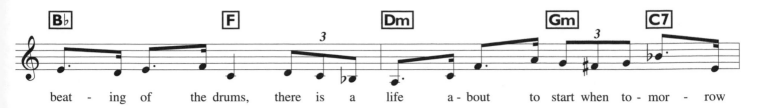

beat - ing of the drums, there is a life a - bout to start when to - mor - row

comes! Will you join in our cru-sade? Who will be strong and stand by me? Be -

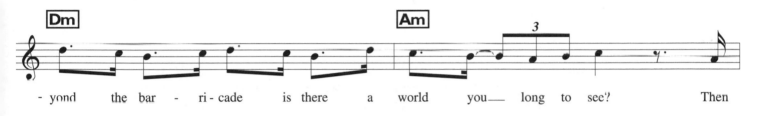

- yond the bar - ri - cade is there a world you— long to see? Then

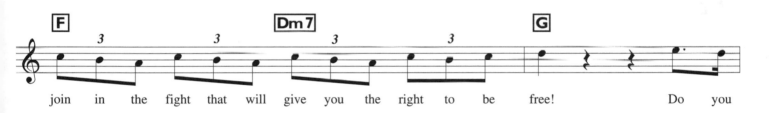

join in the fight that will give you the right to be free! Do you

hear the peo - ple sing? Sing-ing the song of an - gry men. It is the mu - sic of a peo - ple who will

not be slaves a - gain! When the beat - ing of your heart ech - oes the

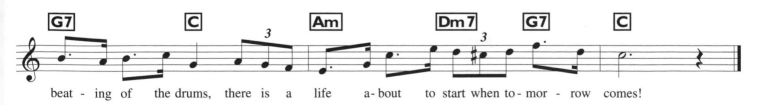

beat - ing of the drums, there is a life a - bout to start when to - mor - row comes!

# DON'T CRY FOR ME ARGENTINA

*Music by Andrew Lloyd Webber*
*Lyrics by Tim Rice*

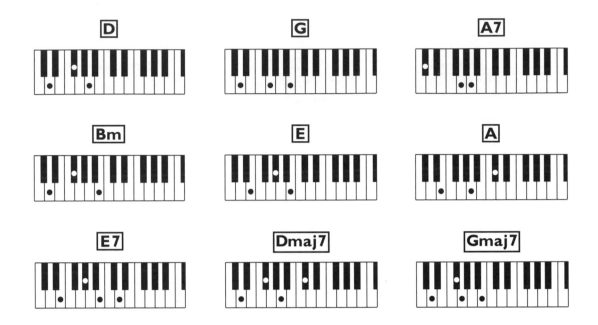

Voice: **Jazz Organ**

Rhythm: **16 Beat**

Tempo: ♩ = 88

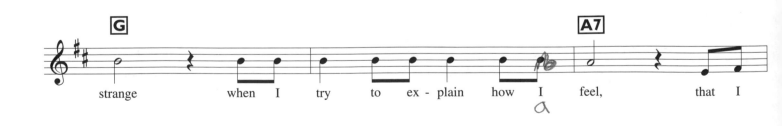

It won't be ea - sy, you'll think it

strange when I try to ex - plain how I feel, that I

still need your love af - ter all that I've done.____ You won't be -

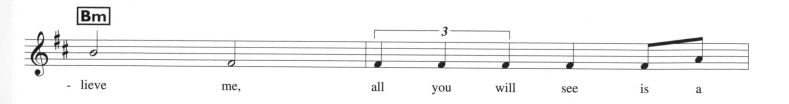

-lieve me, all you will see is a

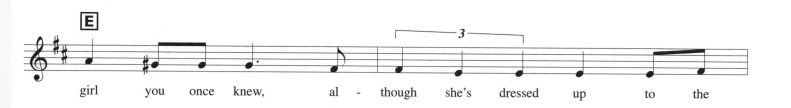

girl you once knew, al - though she's dressed up to the

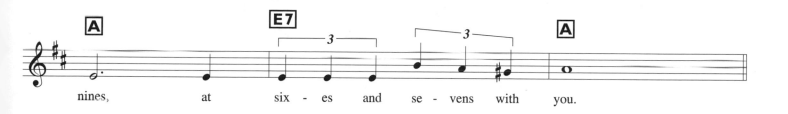

nines, at six - es and se - vens with you.

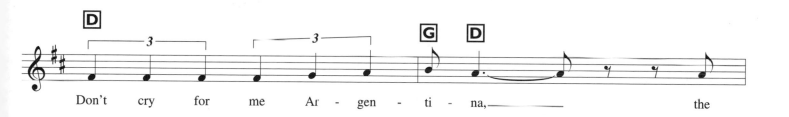

Don't cry for me Ar - gen - ti - na,_____ the

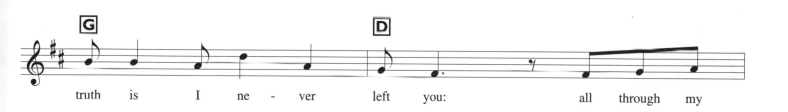

truth is I ne - ver left you: all through my

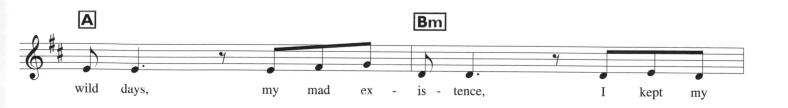

wild days, my mad ex - is - tence, I kept my

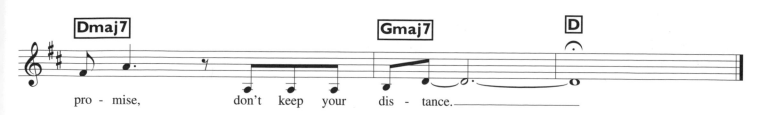

pro - mise, don't keep your dis - tance._____

# EDELWEISS

**Words by Oscar Hammerstein II**
**Music by Richard Rodgers**

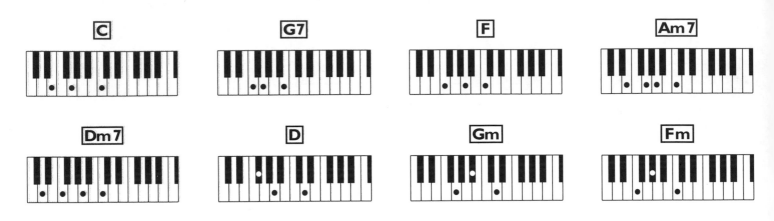

Voice: **Flute**

Rhythm: **Jazz Waltz**

Tempo: ♩ = 108

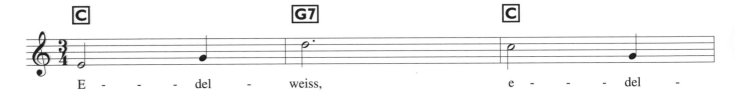

E - - del - weiss, e - del -

- weiss, ev - - 'ry morn - ing you

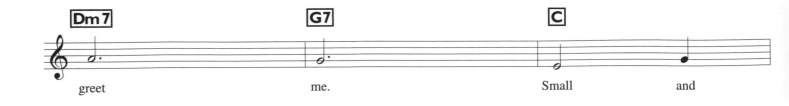

greet me. Small and

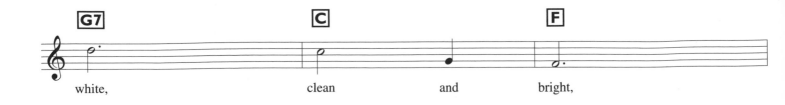

white, clean and bright,

# I DON'T KNOW HOW TO LOVE HIM

*Music by Andrew Lloyd Webber*
*Lyrics by Tim Rice*

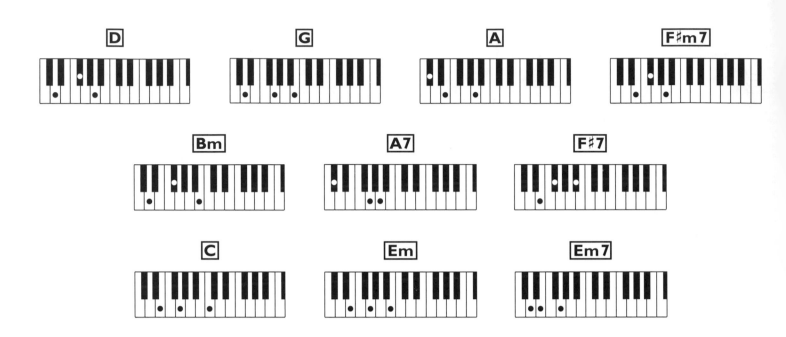

Voice: **Strings**
Rhythm: **Ballad**
Tempo: ♩ = 84

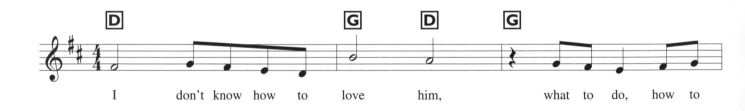

I don't know how to love him, what to do, how to

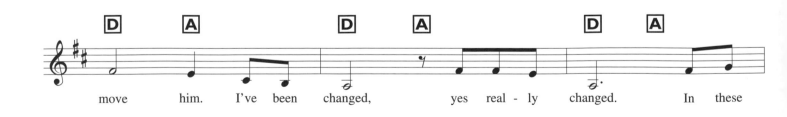

move him. I've been changed, yes real-ly changed. In these

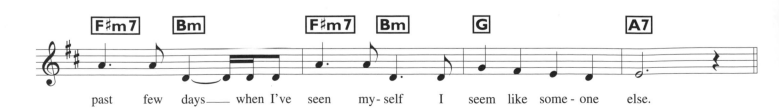

past few days— when I've seen my-self I seem like some-one else.

# I KNOW HIM SO WELL

**Words & Music by Benny Andersson, Tim Rice & Bjorn Ulvaeus**

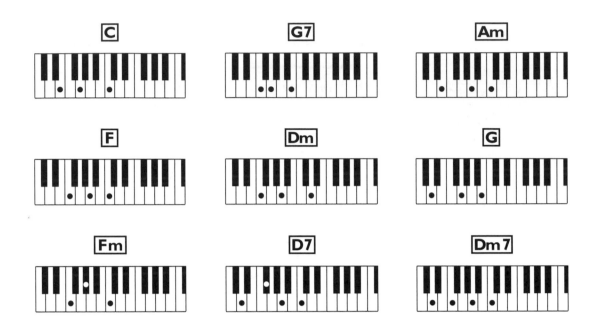

Voice: **Strings**

Rhythm: **Ballad**

Tempo: ♩ = 80

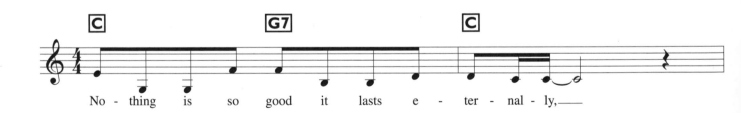

No - thing is so good it lasts e - ter - nal - ly,____

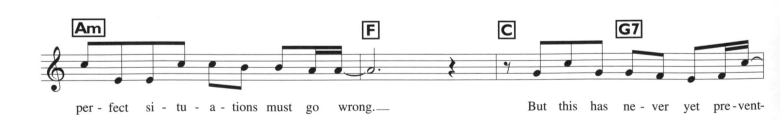

per - fect si - tu - a - tions must go wrong.____ But this has ne - ver yet pre-vent-

- ed me____ want - ing far too much for far too long.

Look-ing back I could have played it dif-ferent-ly,— won a few more mo-ments, who can tell.

But it took time to un-der-stand— the man.—

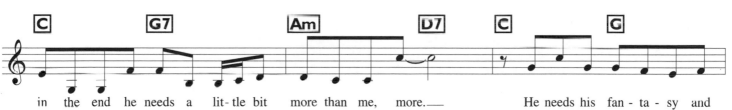

Now at least I know I know him well. Was-n't it good?— Oh, so good!— Was-n't he fine?

— Oh, so fine.— Is-n't it mad-ness he won't be mine?— But

in the end he needs a lit-tle bit more than me, more.— He needs his fan-ta-sy and

free-dom. I know him so— well. It took time to un-der-stand him.

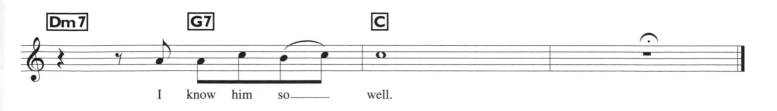

I know him so— well.

# I WHISTLE A HAPPY TUNE

**Words by Oscar Hammerstein II**
**Music by Richard Rodgers**

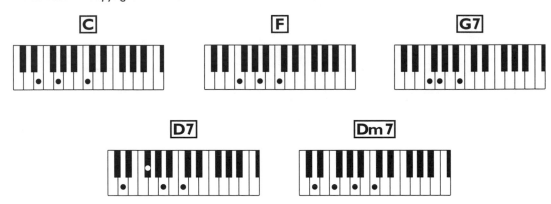

Voice: **Clarinet**

Rhythm: **Enka**

Tempo: ♩ = 80

When - ev - er I feel a -

- fraid, I hold my head e - rect and

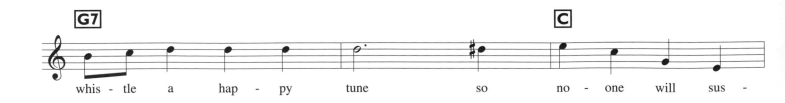

whis - tle a hap - py tune so no - one will sus -

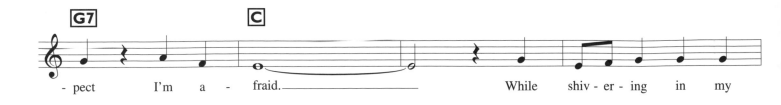

- pect I'm a - fraid. While shiv - er - ing in my

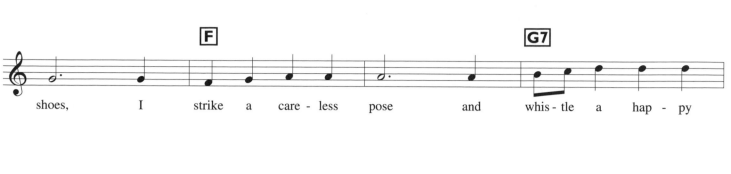

shoes, I strike a care-less pose and whis-tle a hap-py

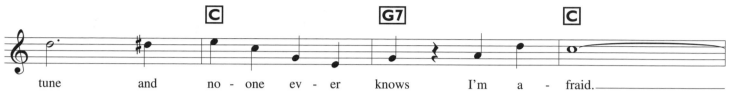

tune and no-one ev-er knows I'm a-fraid.

Make be-lieve you're brave and the trick will take you

far. You may be as brave as you make be-lieve you

are. (Whistle)

You may be as brave

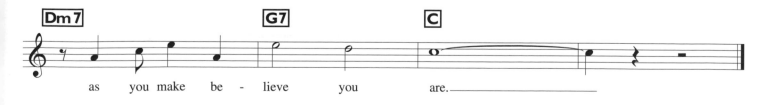

as you make be-lieve you are.

# I'LL NEVER FALL IN LOVE AGAIN

*Words by Hal David*
*Music by Burt Bacharach*

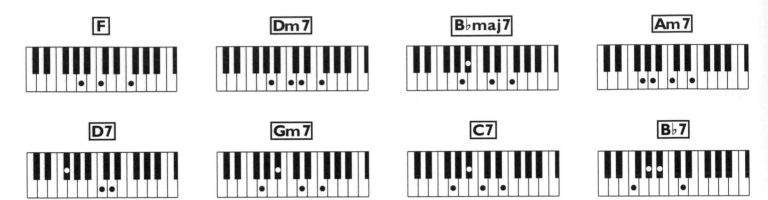

**Voice:** **Electric Piano**
**Rhythm:** **Ballad**
**Tempo:** ♩ = 96

What do you get when you fall in love,_____ a

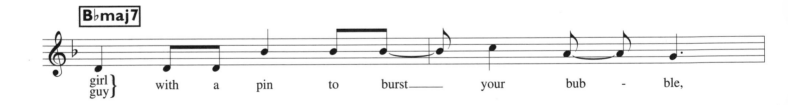

girl } guy }  with a pin to burst_____ your bub - ble,

that's what you get for all your trou - ble,

I'll ne - ver fall in love a -

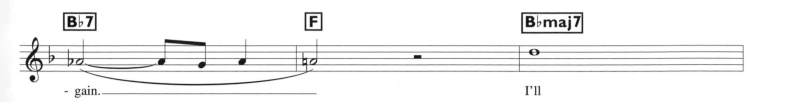

- gain._____ I'll

ne - ver fall in love a - gain._____

What do you get when you fall in love,\_\_\_\_\_ you

on - ly get lies and pain\_\_\_\_ and sor - row, so, for at least un -

- til to - mor - row, I'll ne - ver fall in love a -

- gain._____ I'll

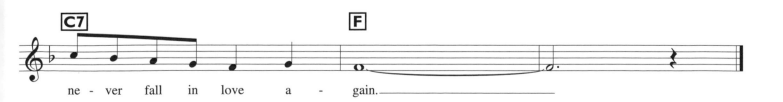

ne - ver fall in love a - gain._____

# IF MY FRIENDS COULD SEE ME NOW

**Words by Dorothy Fields**
**Music by Cy Coleman**
© Copyright 1965 by Dorothy Fields and Cy Coleman.
Rights assigned to Notable Music Company Incorporated in co-publication with Lida Enterprises Incorporated.
Campbell Connelly & Company Limited, 8/9 Frith Street, London W1V 5TZ.
All Rights Reserved. International Copyright Secured.

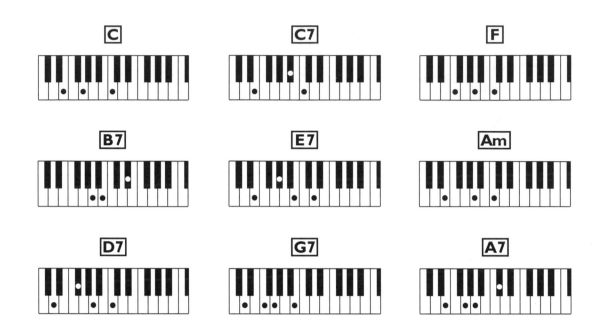

Voice: **Clarinet**

Rhythm: **Enca**

Tempo: ♩ = 116

If they could see me now, that lit - tle

gang of mine, I'm eat - ing fan - cy chow and drink - ing

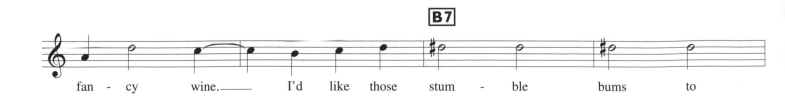

fan - cy wine. I'd like those stum - ble bums to

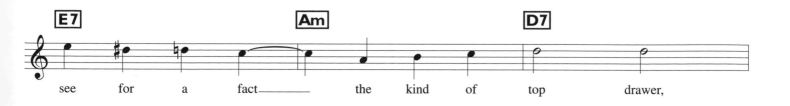

see for a fact_____ the kind of top drawer,

first rate chums I at - tract._____ All I can

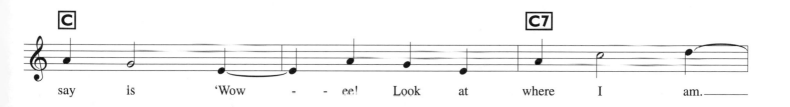

say is 'Wow - - ee! Look at where I am._____

_____ To - night I land - ed, pow!_____ Right in a

pot of jam.'_____ What a set up!

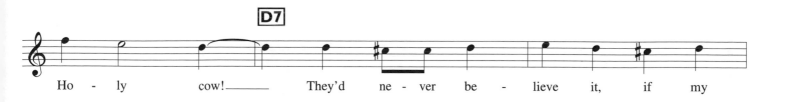

Ho - ly cow!_____ They'd ne - ver be - lieve it, if my

friends could see me now._____

# MARIA

**Music by Leonard Bernstein**
**Lyrics by Stephen Sondheim**

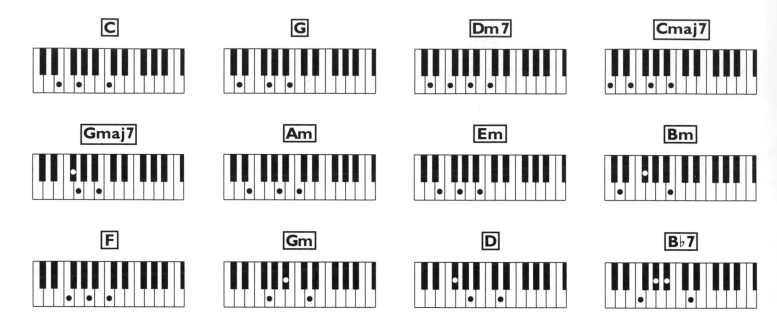

Voice: **Trumpet**
Rhythm: **Samba**
Tempo: ♩ = 96

Ma - ri - a,_____ I've just met a girl called Ma -

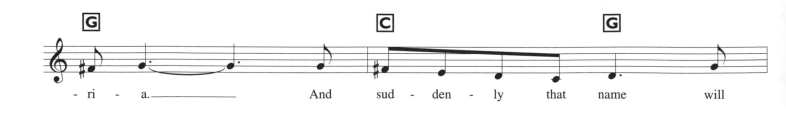

- ri - a._____ And sud - den - ly that name will

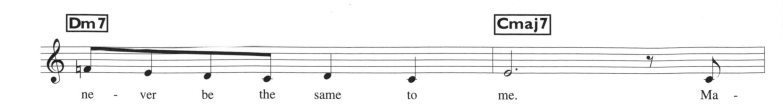

ne - ver be the same to me. Ma -

- ri - a!_____ I've just kissed a girl named Ma -

- ri - a._____ And sud - den - ly I've found how

won - der - ful a sound can be! Ma - -

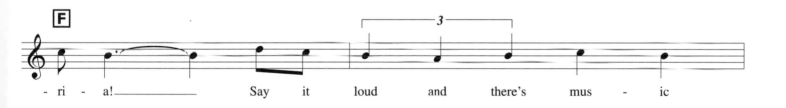

- ri - a!_____ Say it loud and there's mus - ic

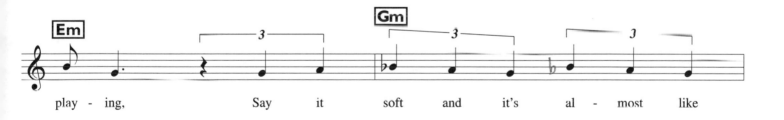

play - ing, Say it soft and it's al - most like

pray - ing._____ Ma - ri - a,_____ I'll

ne - ver stop say - ing 'Ma - ri - a.'_____

# MY FAVOURITE THINGS

*Words by Oscar Hammerstein II*
*Music by Richard Rodgers*

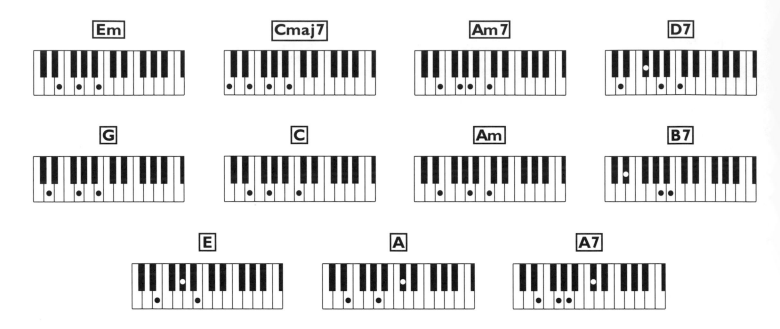

Voice: **Vibraphone**

Rhythm: **Jazz Waltz**

Tempo: ♩ = 144

Rain - drops on ro - ses and whisk - ers on

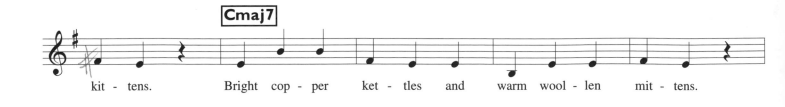

kit - tens. Bright cop - per ket - tles and warm wool - len mit - tens.

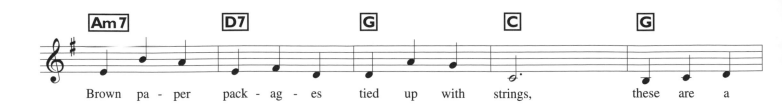

Brown pa - per pack - ag - es tied up with strings, these are a

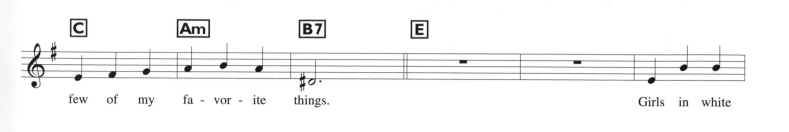

few of my fa - vor - ite things.                          Girls in white

dres - ses with blue sat - in sash - es.   Snow - flakes that stay on my

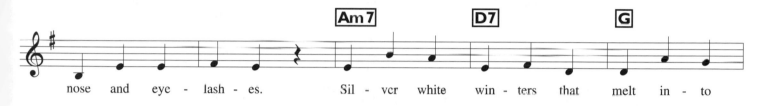

nose and eye - lash - es.   Sil - ver white win - ters that melt in - to

springs,        these are a few of my fa - vor - ite things.

When the dog bites, when the bee stings, when I'm feel - ing

sad,_____    I sim - ply re - mem - ber my fa - vor - ite things and then I don't

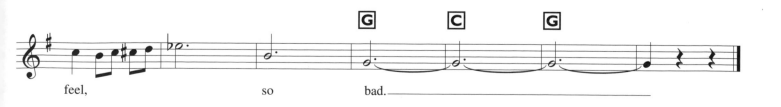

feel,         so bad._____

# ONCE IN A LIFETIME

*Words & Music by Leslie Bricusse & Anthony Newley*

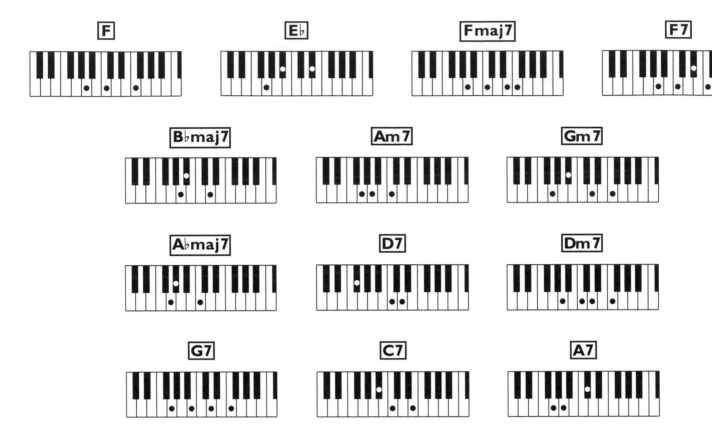

Voice: **Trumpet**

Rhythm: **16 Beat**

Tempo: ♩ = **92**

Just once in a life-time___ a man knows a mo-ment,___ one

won-der-ful mo-ment___ when fate takes a hand.___ And

this is my mo - ment,_____ my once in a life - time_____ when

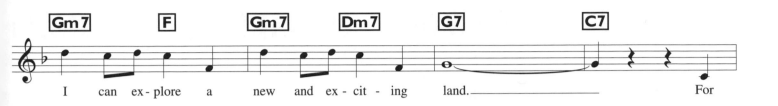

I can ex - plore a new and ex - cit - ing land._____ For

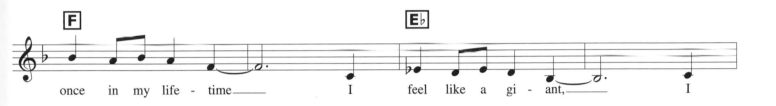

once in my life - time_____ I feel like a gi - ant,_____ I

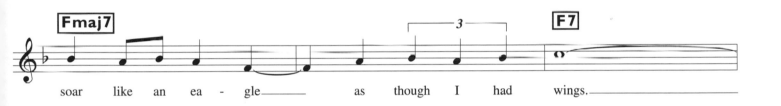

soar like an ea - gle_____ as though I had wings._____

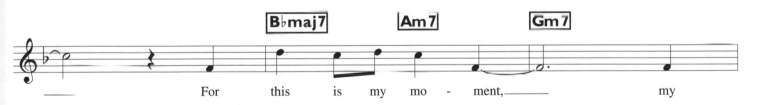

_____ For this is my mo - ment,_____ my

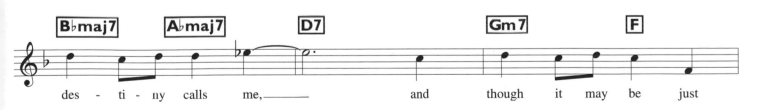

des - ti - ny calls me,_____ and though it may be just

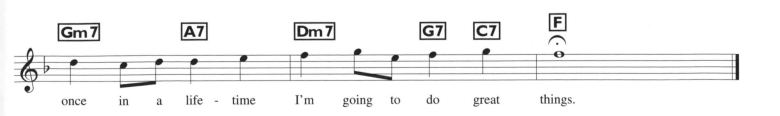

once in a life - time I'm going to do great things.

# PEOPLE WILL SAY WE'RE IN LOVE

*Words by Oscar Hammerstein II*
*Music by Richard Rodgers*

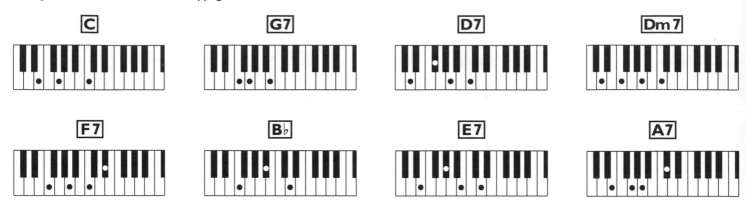

Voice: **Jazz Organ**

Rhythm: **Enka**

Tempo: ♩ = 120

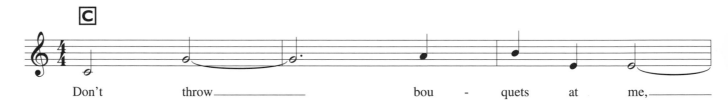

Don't throw_____ bou - quets at me,_____

_____ don't please_____ my

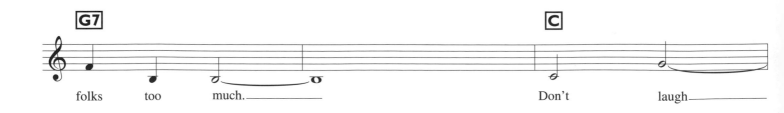

folks too much._____ Don't laugh_____

_____ at my jokes too much._____

Peo - ple will say we're in love._____

_____ Don't start_____ col - lect - ing things,_____

_____ give me my rose and my

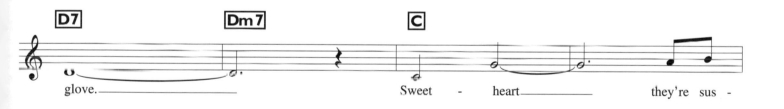

glove._____ Sweet - heart_____ they're sus -

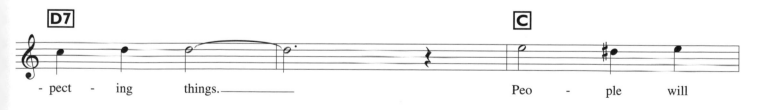

- pect - ing things._____ Peo - ple will

say we're in love._____

# SEVENTY SIX TROMBONES

**Words & Music by Meredith Willson**

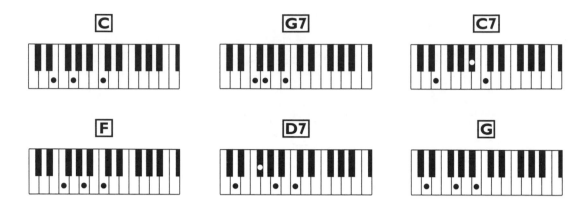

Voice: **Trumpet**

Rhythm: **Shuffle**

Tempo: ♩. = 120

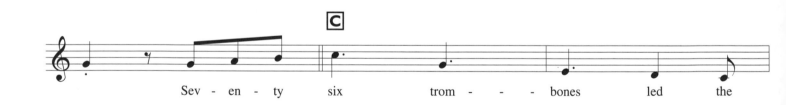

Sev - en - ty    six    trom - - - bones    led    the

big    pa - rade,_____ with    a    hun - dred    and    ten    cor - - -

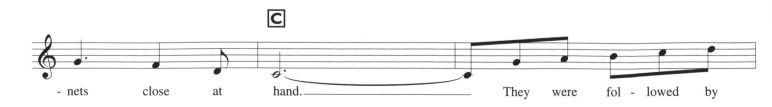

- nets    close    at    hand._____ They    were    fol - lowed    by

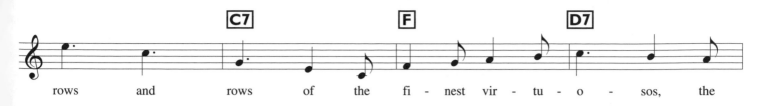

rows and rows of the fi - nest vir - tu - o - sos, the

cream of ev - 'ry fa - mous band.

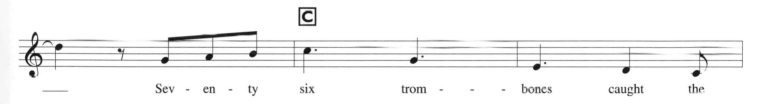

Sev - en - ty six trom - - - bones caught the

morn - ing sun, with a hun - dred and ten cor - -

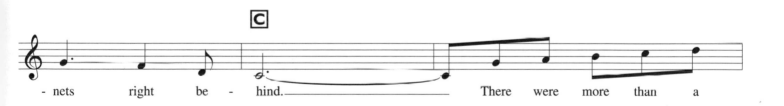

- nets right be - hind. There were more than a

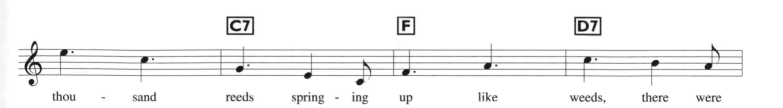

thou - sand reeds spring - ing up like weeds, there were

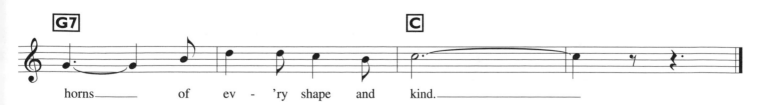

horns of ev - 'ry shape and kind.

# SMOKE GETS IN YOUR EYES

*Music by Jerome Kern*
*Words by Otto Harbach*

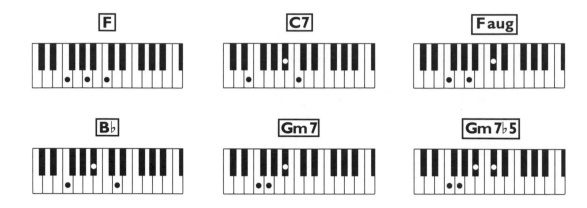

Voice: **Jazz Organ**

Rhythm: **16 beat**

Tempo: ♩ **= 76**

They asked me how I

knew my true love was true._____

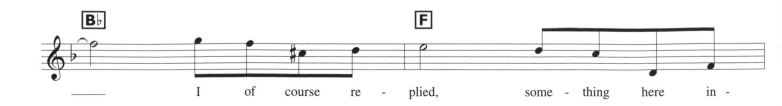

_____ I of course re - plied, some - thing here in-

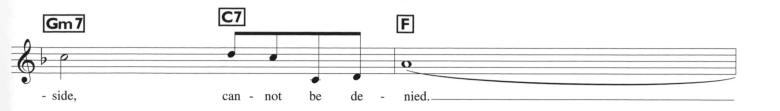

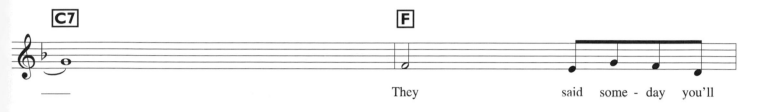

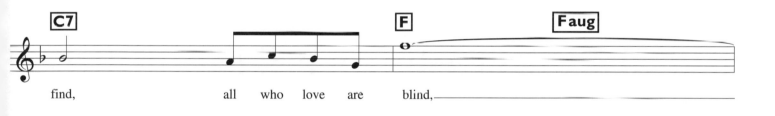

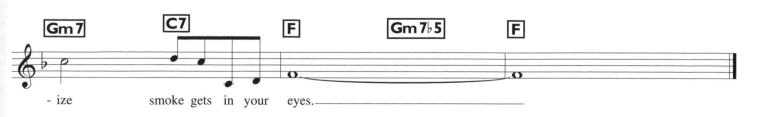

# SOMEWHERE

**Music by Leonard Bernstein**
**Lyrics by Stephen Sondheim**

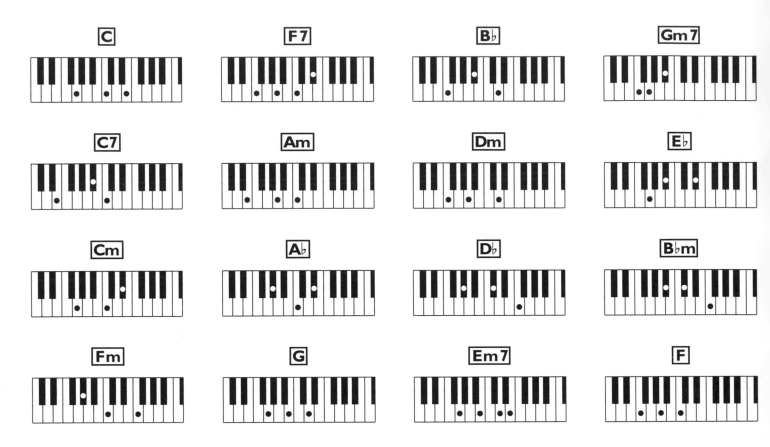

Voice: **Flute**

Rhythm: **Ballad**

Tempo: ♩ = 76

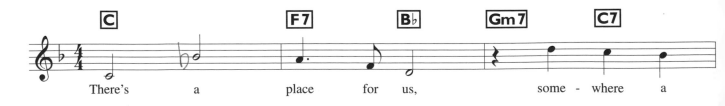

There's a place for us, some-where a

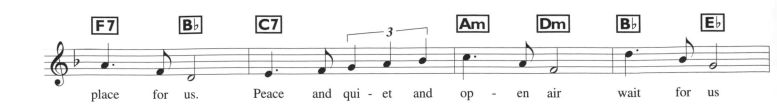

place for us. Peace and qui - et and op - en air wait for us

# SUPERSTAR

*Music by Andrew Lloyd Webber*
*Lyrics by Tim Rice*

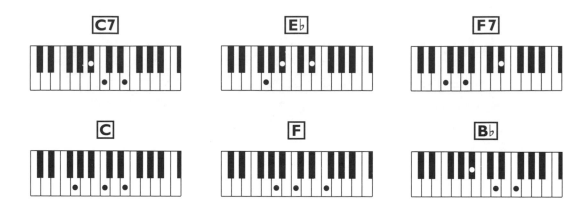

Voice: **Jazz Organ**

Rhythm: **8 beat**

Tempo: ♩ = 104

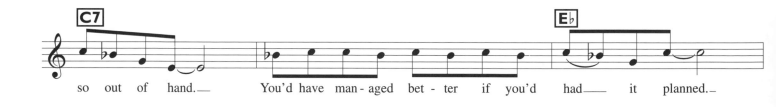

Ev - 'ry-time I look at you I don't un-der-stand — why you let the things you did get

so out of hand. — You'd have man - aged bet - ter if you'd had — it planned. —

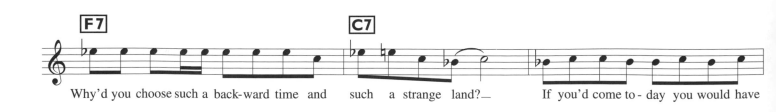

Why'd you choose such a back-ward time and such a strange land? — If you'd come to - day you would have

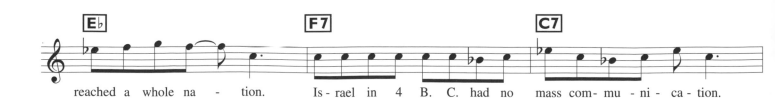

reached a whole na - tion. Is - rael in 4 B. C. had no mass com - mu - ni - ca - tion.

# TILL THERE WAS YOU

*Words & Music by Meredith Willson*

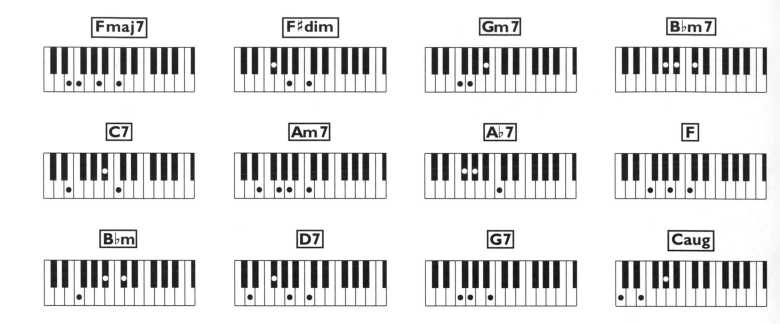

Voice: **Jazz Organ**

Rhythm: **Ballad**

Tempo: ♩ = 92

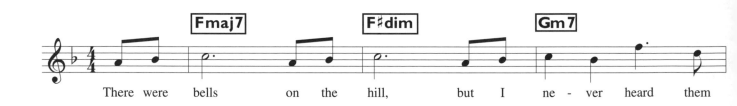

There were bells on the hill, but I ne - ver heard them

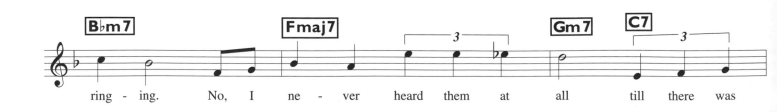

ring - ing. No, I ne - ver heard them at all till there was

you.___ There were birds in the sky, but I

ne - ver saw them wing - ing. No, I ne - ver saw them at

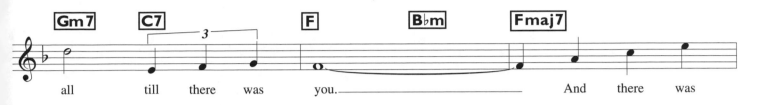

all till there was you. And there was

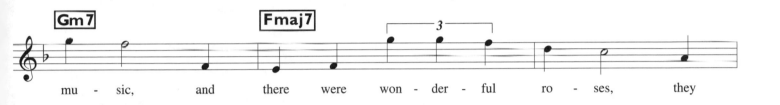

mu - sic, and there were won - der - ful ro - ses, they

tell me in sweet fra - grant mea - dows of

dawn and dew. There was love all a -

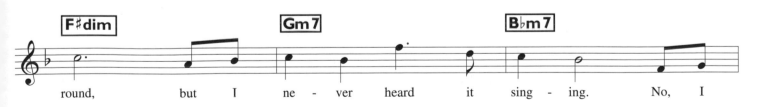

round, but I ne - ver heard it sing - ing. No, I

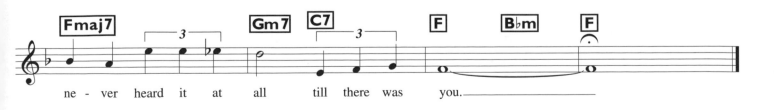

ne - ver heard it at all till there was you.

# WHO CAN I TURN TO?

*Words & Music by Leslie Bricusse & Anthony Newley*

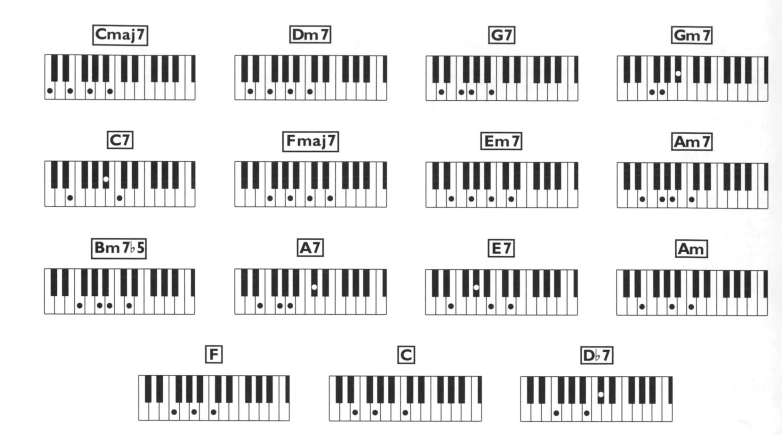

Voice: **Piano**

Rhythm: **16 beat**

Tempo: ♩ = **100**

Who can I turn to _____ when no-bo-dy needs me?

_____ My heart wants to know and so I must go where

des - ti - ny leads me._____ With no star to guide me_____ and

no - one be - side me,_____ I'll go on my way and

af - ter the day the dark - ness will hide me._____ And

may - be to - mor - row_____ I'll find what I'm af - ter,_____ I'll

throw off my sor - row, beg steal or bor - row my share of laugh - ter._____

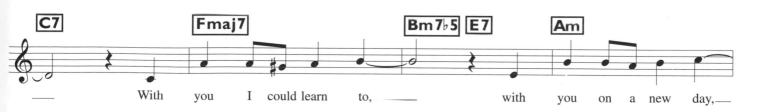

_____ With you I could learn to, _____ with you on a new day,_____

_____ but who can I turn to if you turn a - way?

# EASIEST KEYBOARD COLLECTION

Easy-to-play melody line arrangements for all keyboards with chord symbols and lyric. Suggested registration, rhythm and tempo are included for each song together with keyboard diagrams showing left-hand chord voicings used.

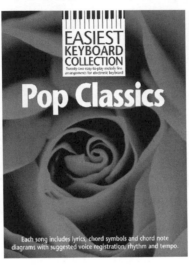

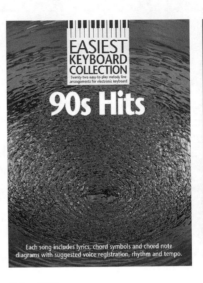

### Showstoppers
Consider Yourself (Oliver!), Do You Hear The People Sing? (Les Misérables), I Know Him So Well (Chess), Maria (West Side Story), Smoke Gets In Your Eyes (Roberta) and 17 more big stage hits.
**Order No. AM944218**

### Pop Classics
A Whiter Shade Of Pale (Procol Harum), Bridge Over Troubled Water (Simon & Garfunkel), Crocodile Rock (Elton John) and 19 more classic hit songs, including Hey Jude (The Beatles), Imagine (John Lennon), and Massachusetts (The Bee Gees).
**Order No. AM944196**

### 90s Hits
Over 20 of the greatest hits of the 1990s, including Always (Bon Jovi), Fields Of Gold (Sting), Have I Told You Lately (Rod Stewart), One Sweet Day (Mariah Carey), Say You'll Be There (Spice Girls), and Wonderwall (Oasis).
**Order No. AM944229**

### Abba
A great collection of 22 Abba hit songs. Includes Dancing Queen, Fernand I Have A Dream, Mamm. Mia, Super Trouper, Take Chance On Me, Thank Y For The Music, The Winr Takes It All, and Waterloo
**Order No. AM959860**

## Also available...

**...plus many more!**